Christian Mandalas™

The Great Reversal

Kerry M. Pierce

Christian Mandalas[†]

The Great Reversal

Kerry M. Pierce

All images Copyright Kerry M. Pierce unless noted otherwise

www.KerryPierce.com

www.ChristianMandalas.com

[†]Christian Mandalas is a trademark of Kerry M. Pierce

ISBN-13: 978-0-9972809-8-2

Cover Image: The Penitent Thief

While there is life, there is hope.

The Penitent Thief is a Christian mandala I created over a long period while reflecting on the crucifixion passage in Luke 23. The focus of the image comes from verse 43, where Jesus tells the penitent thief on the cross next to him that he would be with our Lord in paradise that day.

The image is surreal, disorienting at first, but it entices us to ask questions and explore.

The lower hand is that of the penitent criminal in Luke 23. This criminal, crucified next to Jesus, is sometimes referred to as Dismas. The middle hand is that of the second thief crucified next to Jesus. Finally, the top hand is Jesus'.

Dismas was a criminal, a malefactor, a doer of evil. Sentenced to death, Dismas was at the bottom of the first-century Palestinian society.

On the cross, next to Jesus, something remarkable happened. Dismas confessed his sin and declared Jesus to be innocent. Next, he gave us the first direct expression of faith in the dying Messiah. This half-dead, corrupt man, surged forward in faith to rely on the grace of Christ.

This moment is summarized in the mandala with the drop of blood the fell from the hand of Christ. The second thief chooses to allow the blood of Christ to pass him by. The believing, repentant Dismas reaches out to receive Christ's blood.

Made clean by his faith in Christ's work, Dismas joined Jesus in paradise.

Despite his background, Dismas believed in Jesus, and he was saved. Dismas, almost literally, made his decision for Christ at the last minute.

Contents

Acknowledgments

Special thanks to my wife Nancy and my daughter Kirsten for their support, insights, reviews, and suggestions.

1 Christian Mandala Review

Before you begin

Before you begin, it's good to have a little background. The process itself is very straightforward. These studies are intended to focus you on Scripture rather than make you constantly refer back to the process. In other words, the intention is to focus on God's word rather than asking yourself: "Am I doing this right?"

If you've read the book, heard the lecture, or watched the introduction video, you are probably good to go. If you want a quick review, read on.

Why Christian Mandalas?

Information gathered from over 1000 churches shows that the best way to move Christians forward as disciples of Christ, to make them more Christ-like, is to have them read and reflect on Scripture.

Prayer, Sermons, alone time, tithing, and fasting, are excellent as well, but reading and reflecting on Scripture is at the top of the list. If there was only one thing you could do to grow in Christ, spending time in Scripture would be it. This practice has been borne out in my personal experience as well.

Our study books are the killer app to help people read and reflect on Scripture. At an elementary level, you draw as you read Scripture. You just need to draw at any level. If you can play Pictionary, that is good enough. Sharing your artwork in a small group environment will lead to learning, laughing, and participating.

This study book also contains great reversal-specific drawing resources. It also includes great reversal-specific commentary and fine art resources to help you dig into Scripture more deeply.

Your resulting mandalas will serve as a visual summary of Scripture that will stay with you throughout the day. The process of drawing from Scripture often enables new revelations because you are working with the Third Person of the Trinity on a one-on-one basis. The result is accelerated Christ-like transformation.

Tips

Don't worry if you "can't draw." Drawing ability isn't critical. The process still works. Substitute words if you need to to keep things spontaneous. I have drawn up a number of simple elements that often appear in these texts together with basic Christian Symbols. They are in the back of the book for reference. Feel free to copy them. A little color can help. Feel free to erase. It's not a sin.

For some people, it's important to share what they've done. Sharing invigorates them. If this is true for you, find a way to do this. The studies work well in a small group setting.

FAQs are found at **www.kerrypierce.com** and **www.christianmandalas.com**.

You will also find my blog and links for online sharing of your mandalas on the website.

The Mechanics

For each Scripture, you will see three circles for your mandalas. You will spend three days per Scripture, drawing a new mandala for that Scripture each day. It works best if you spend three consecutive days on the Scripture. If life gets in the way, and you miss a day, don't throw the study book away. Just pick up where you left off.

Each of the three days takes a slightly different approach to the Scripture. Day 1 is a Spontaneous day. Day 2 is a Rational thinking day. Day 3 is another Spontaneous day after your mind has had some time to process the thoughts from day 1 and day 2. See Figure 1.

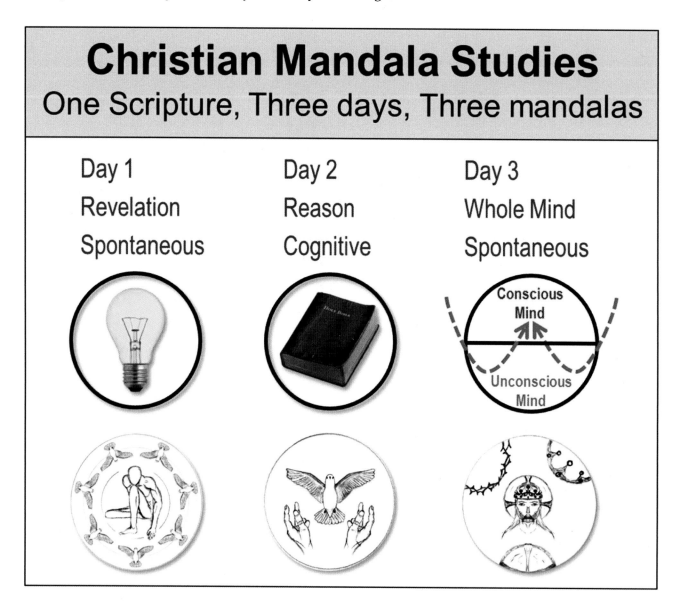

Figure 1

The day 1 mandala is a Revelational day. You read the Scripture and draw spontaneously. I typically start by praying and then reading the passage slowly. Let the Holy Spirit speak to you: a word, a phrase, a sentence, or a concept. Draw as the concept or concepts unfold. **Spontaneously** translate them to imagery and symbols in the mandala. Don't analyze. The key is to start drawing the mandala, trying to focus on a central point. See Figure 2.

Day 1

Figure 2: Example of completed day 1

The day 2 mandala is a Rational or Reasoning day. Again, it's good to start by praying and then reading the passage slowly. You will read the same Scripture but think about it before drawing. Sometimes I read it out loud, and it works better for me. It is helpful to have a commentary or access to the internet for this day. Go ahead and begin by digging through a commentary (hard copy or online) or look at works of art. There are suggested resources in the back of the book if you need a starting place. Eventually, you will find the resources that work best for you. After thinking (using your cognitive abilities), go ahead and draw the day 2 mandala. People often come up with something entirely different than day 1. See Figure 3.

Day 2

Figure 3: Example of completed days 1 and 2

The day 3 mandala is the Whole Mind day. The day you integrate everything that has been simmering in your conscious mind along with the insights that have bubbled up from your unconscious mind. Start by praying and then reading the Scripture again for the third time. This day is also a spontaneous day. Your mind has had two days and nights to soak in this text. Take all the imagery coming from the Holy Spirit's revelation and your studies and then draw as the concepts unfold, spontaneously translating them into imagery and symbols in the mandala. See Figure 4.

Day 3

Figure 4: Example of completed days 1, 2 and 3

Day 3 is often a high point for people. I find myself dreaming the Scriptures sometimes or at the very least waking up in the morning on day 3 with a fresh new insight. Day 3 is my favorite.

Figure 5 gives an overall summary of the process. Think of the process as guidelines. Get hung up on the Scripture, not the process.

OK, you are ready to begin.

Christian Mandala Bible Studies

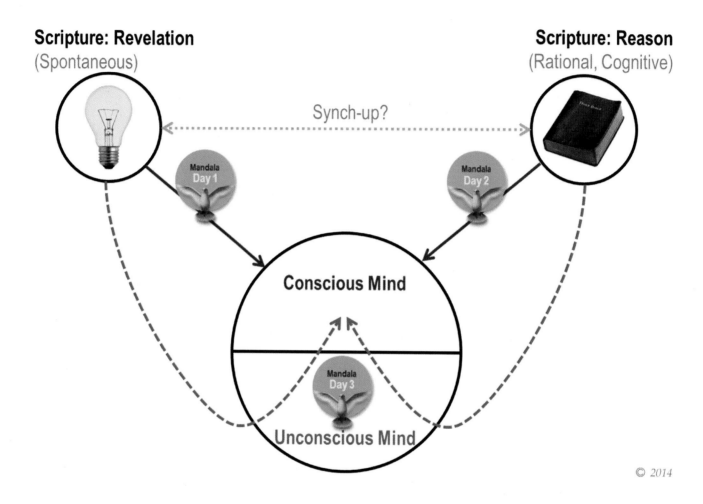

Figure 5

2 The Great Reversal Introduction

In the Gospel of Luke, we find a recurrent theme that theologians refer to as the great reversal. These are unexpected, almost shocking statements from Jesus that cause us to stop and re-think our value systems. Sayings like: "Love your enemies," "whoever would save his life will lose it, but whoever loses his life for my sake will save it," "some are last who will be first, and some are first who will be last," "It is more blessed to give than to receive," and "For everyone who exalts himself will be humbled, but the one who humbles himself will be exalted."

Perhaps the most notable great reversal occurs when the penitent thief on the cross rises from the bottom of the first-century Palestinian ecosystem and expresses his faith in Christ. He repents, and without the benefit of the Lord's instruction which the apostles enjoyed, he reaches out in faith, requesting Jesus to remember him when Jesus enters into his reign. A criminal, hours away from death and in pain, suddenly has the presence of mind to confess his sin and his faith in Jesus. Spiritual whiplash.

These great reversal sayings challenge us. "Love your enemies." That is not easy. Reflecting on these great reversal sayings is often humbling. But God reminds us that he honors the humble, that the humble will be exalted.

In the great reversal study, we find that the value system of the Kingdom is much different than that of our culture. The great reversal challenges us to focus on the Kingdom rather than the world. We are called to use our energy, our love, and our gifts for the Kingdom.

When reflected upon and applied to our lives, the great reversal sayings cause our focus to shift from our needs to the needs of others.

There is reassurance. Reassurance that the Kingdom we are giving ourselves to, like our souls, is eternal and has eternal value.

Finally, note that Jesus is a master teacher. In his great reversal statements, Jesus often uses parallelism. He pairs similar sayings for emphasis, and he pairs opposite sayings to highlight the contrast between them. The result is that the truth that Jesus is communicating is articulated more vividly than if he had used ordinary speech.

In the visual realm, repetition and contrast are also used to intensify the idea conveyed by a work of art visually. The Dutch graphic artist M. C. Escher made extensive use of this technique in his work with tessellations. As a result, the great reversal teachings of Jesus naturally translate into the visual realm and the mandala format.

Creating mandalas for these teachings will deepen your understanding of the great reversal and help you apply Jesus' teaching to your life.

Final Notes

This study uses the **ESV** translation of the Bible for the great reversal texts. Feel free to use a different translation. The **KJV** and **NRSV** are also excellent. **The Message** is contemporary and maybe more understandable for some. BlueLetterBible.org allows one to see more than a dozen different translations of the Bible on a verse-by-verse basis.

Heaven and Hell Mandala
Kerry Pierce - Homage to Escher

3 The Great Reversal Study

The following pages are the contents of the study. Rather than filling in the blanks, you are going to fill in the circles. The visual process is very powerful. At the end of the study, you will look back and revel in what you have created and the understanding that has come to you.

The passages are packed with vivid contrasts, imagery, and meaning. Some of the passages are short. On day 2, feel free to expand around the text to look at the context.

Some of the passages are longer. Feel free to focus on a single word, phrase, or concept on the first day.

The studies you are about to begin are not two-minute, microwaveable, instant Spiritual junk food that allows you to check off your God-thing for the day. We are building spiritual muscle mass. You will transform and become more Christ-like.

Save your study books when you are done. It's fun to go back and see what you did and how you have progressed.

Figure 7 below shows what I typically have available when I work. A pencil and eraser are essential. The other items are helpful. A small set of colored pencils helps to color in more challenging elements such as water and light.

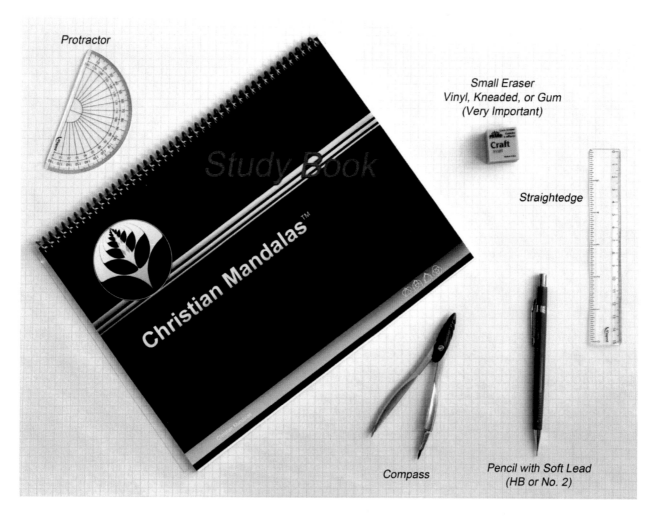

Figure 7

Introductory Reversal – Luke 2:7 (ESV)

[7] And she gave birth to her firstborn son and wrapped him in swaddling cloths and laid him in a manger, because there was no place for them in the inn.

Day 1
Revelation
Spontaneous

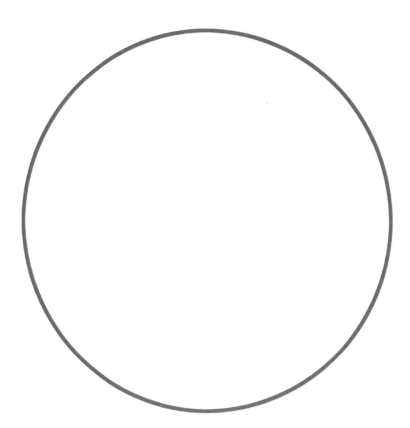

Luke 6:27-28

27 "But I say to you who hear, Love your enemies, do good to those who hate you, 28 bless those who curse you, pray for those who abuse you."

Day 1
Revelation
Spontaneous

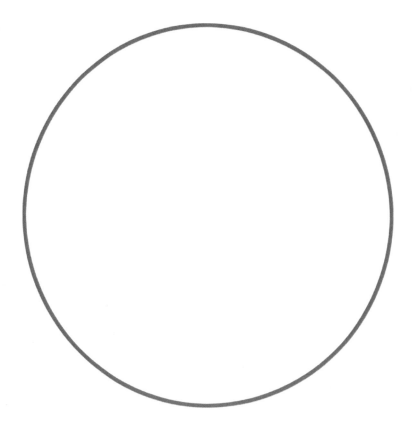

Day 2
Reason
Cognitive

Day 3
Whole Mind
Spontaneous

Conscious

Unconscious

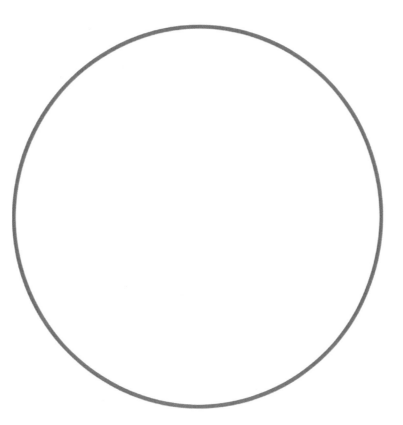

Luke 9:23-26

23 And he said to all, "If anyone would come after me, let him deny himself and take up his cross daily and follow me. 24 For whoever would save his life will lose it, but whoever loses his life for my sake will save it. 25 For what does it profit a man if he gains the whole world and loses or forfeits himself? 26 For whoever is ashamed of me and of my words, of him will the Son of Man be ashamed when he comes in his glory and the glory of the Father and of the holy angels."

Day 1
Revelation
Spontaneous

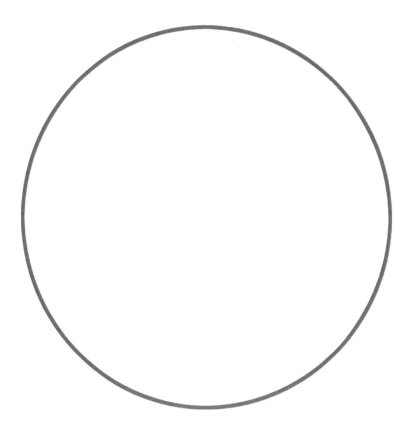

15

²⁵ And behold, a lawyer stood up to put him to the test, saying, "Teacher, what shall I do to inherit eternal life?" ²⁶ He said to him, "What is written in the Law? How do you read it?" ²⁷ And he answered, "You shall love the Lord your God with all your heart and with all your soul and with all your strength and with all your mind, and your neighbor as yourself." ²⁸ And he said to him, "You have answered correctly; do this, and you will live."

²⁹ But he, desiring to justify himself, said to Jesus, "And who is my neighbor?" ³⁰ Jesus replied, "A man was going down from Jerusalem to Jericho, and he fell among robbers, who stripped him and beat him and departed, leaving him half dead. ³¹ Now by chance a priest was going down that road, and when he saw him he passed by on the other side. ³² So likewise a Levite, when he came to the place and saw him, passed by on the other side. ³³ But a Samaritan, as he journeyed, came to where he was, and when he saw him, he had compassion. ³⁴ He went to him and bound up his wounds, pouring on oil and wine. Then he set him on his own animal and brought him to an inn and took care of him. ³⁵ And the next day he took out two denarii and gave them to the innkeeper, saying, 'Take care of him, and whatever more you spend, I will repay you when I come back.' ³⁶ Which of these three, do you think, proved to be a neighbor to the man who fell among the robbers?" ³⁷ He said, "The one who showed him mercy." And Jesus said to him, "You go, and do likewise."

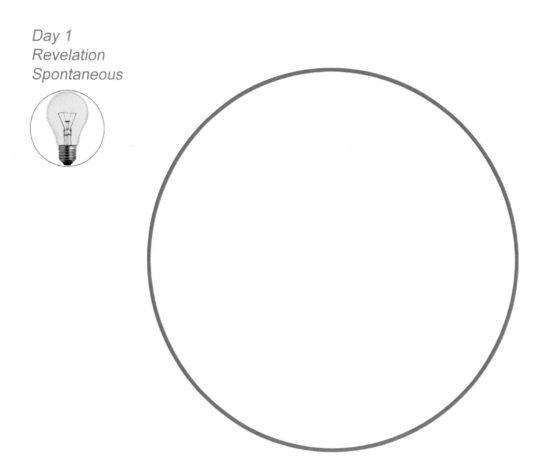

Day 1
Revelation
Spontaneous

Luke 12:16-21

16 And he told them a parable, saying, "The land of a rich man produced plentifully, 17 and he thought to himself, 'What shall I do, for I have nowhere to store my crops?' 18 And he said, 'I will do this: I will tear down my barns and build larger ones, and there I will store all my grain and my goods. 19 And I will say to my soul, "Soul, you have ample goods laid up for many years; relax, eat, drink, be merry."' 20 But God said to him, 'Fool! This night your soul is required of you, and the things you have prepared, whose will they be?' 21 So is the one who lays up treasure for himself and is not rich toward God."

Day 1
Revelation
Spontaneous

[32] "Fear not, little flock, for it is your Father's good pleasure to give you the kingdom. [33] Sell your possessions, and give to the needy. Provide yourselves with moneybags that do not grow old, with a treasure in the heavens that does not fail, where no thief approaches and no moth destroys. [34] For where your treasure is, there will your heart be also."

Day 1
Revelation
Spontaneous

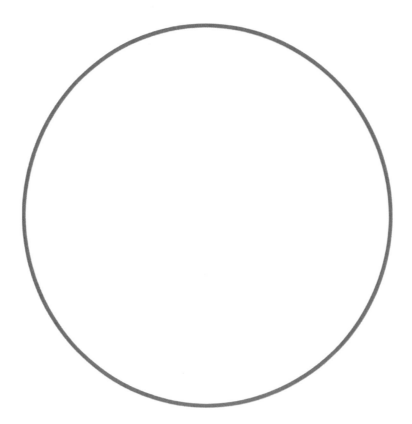

Conscious

Unconscious

21

29 "And people will come from east and west, and from north and south, and recline at table in the kingdom of God. 30 And behold, some are last who will be first, and some are first who will be last."

Day 1
Revelation
Spontaneous

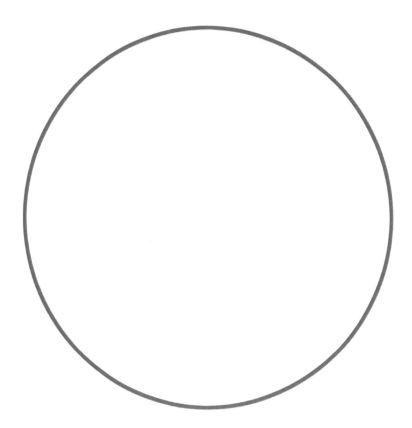

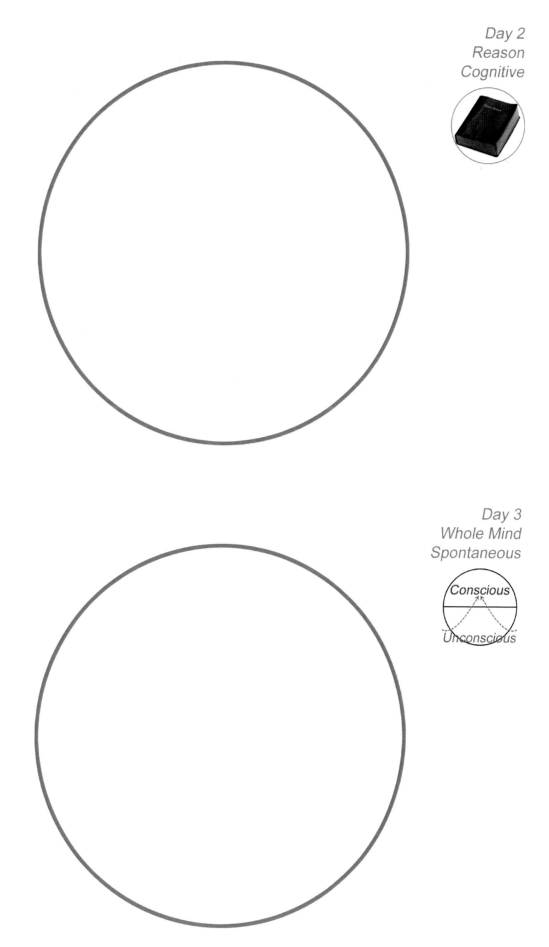

Day 2
Reason
Cognitive

Day 3
Whole Mind
Spontaneous

Conscious

Unconscious

23

⁹ He also told this parable to some who trusted in themselves that they were righteous, and treated others with contempt: ¹⁰ "Two men went up into the temple to pray, one a Pharisee and the other a tax collector. ¹¹ The Pharisee, standing by himself, prayed thus: 'God, I thank you that I am not like other men, extortioners, unjust, adulterers, or even like this tax collector. ¹² I fast twice a week; I give tithes of all that I get.' ¹³ But the tax collector, standing far off, would not even lift up his eyes to heaven, but beat his breast, saying, 'God, be merciful to me, a sinner!' ¹⁴ I tell you, this man went down to his house justified, rather than the other. For everyone who exalts himself will be humbled, but the one who humbles himself will be exalted."

Day 1
Revelation
Spontaneous

Conscious

Unconscious

25

[35] "In all things I have shown you that by working hard in this way we must help the weak and remember the words of the Lord Jesus, how he himself said, 'It is more blessed to give than to receive.'"

Day 1
Revelation
Spontaneous

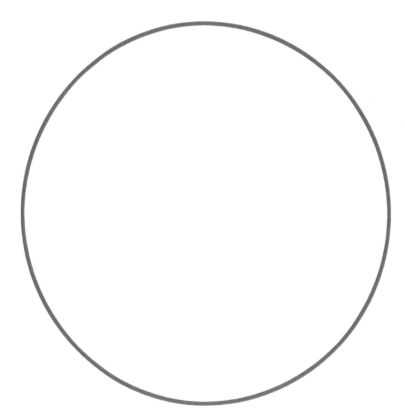

Conscious

Unconscious

39 One of the criminals who were hanged railed at him, saying, "Are you not the Christ? Save yourself and us!" 40 But the other rebuked him, saying, "Do you not fear God, since you are under the same sentence of condemnation? 41 And we indeed justly, for we are receiving the due reward of our deeds; but this man has done nothing wrong." 42 And he said, "Jesus, remember me when you come into your kingdom." 43 And he said to him, "Truly, I say to you, today you will be with me in paradise."

Day 1
Revelation
Spontaneous

Conscious

Unconscious

Symbols

4 Symbol Resources

The Circle is the symbol for God.

The Triangle is the symbol for the Trinity.

The Square is the symbol for the earth, or the four points of the compass.

The Pentagon is the symbol for the five wounds of Christ.

God the Father: Manus Dei - The Hand of God.

The Dove is the symbol for the Holy Spirit.

Jesus: Agnus Dei - The Lamb of God

Trinity Symbols

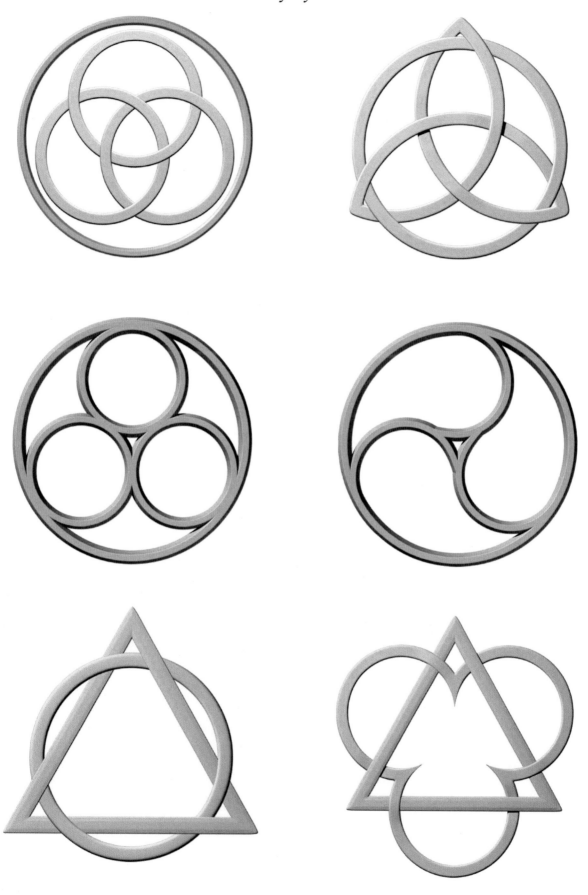

5 Number and Color Resources

One: One is the number of unity, and one God.

Two: Two is the number of duality. The dual nature of Christ, human and divine.

Three: Three is most often used as the number for the Trinity - Father, Son and Holy Spirit.

Four: The number four is usually used to represent the four Evangelists. It may also be used to represent the four corners of the earth or the four seasons.

Five: Five is symbolic of the five wounds Jesus received on the cross.

Six: Six is the number of creation because God created in six days.

Seven: Seven is the number of perfection, completion and rest.

Eight: The number eight represents regeneration or resurrection. It is for this reason that many baptismal fonts are eight-sided.

Nine: Nine is the angelic number because the Bible mentions nine choirs of angels.

Ten: Ten is the number of the Ten Commandments, and Ten Plagues. It is also a completion number.

Twelve: Twelve is the number of the tribes of Israel and the number of Apostles. It is can be used to represent the entire church.

Thirteen: Thirteen is the number of faithlessness and betrayal.

Forty: Forty is used as a number for trial or testing.

Black: Black is symbolic of death and mourning. It is used on Good Friday.

Blue: Blue, the color of the sky, is symbolic of heaven and also truth.

Brown: Brown is the color of spiritual death and degradation.

Gray: Gray is the color of ash, and so is used to represent repentance, mourning and humility. It may be used during Lent.

Green: Green is the color of new plant life in Spring. Green is the color used during Epiphany. It also represents regeneration.

Purple: Purple is the color of royalty. It is also used for the seasons of Advent and Lent.

Red: Red is the color of blood, and is used as the color for the commemoration of martyred saints. It is used as the color for Pentecost.

White: White is the color of purity, innocence, and holiness. It is the liturgical color for the Christmas and Easter seasons.

Yellow: Yellow is a color that serves a dual purpose. As the color of light, yellow may be used to represent divinity. However, because yellow light is not pure white, it may also be used to symbolize corruption and degradation.

6 Drawing Common Elements

Here are some simple drawings to help with your mandalas. These are not intended as a how-to-draw study. They are simply a resource to provide image references to copy if you are new to drawing. Since the focus is to move quickly on the spontaneous days, my drawings are less detailed on those days, especially day 1. I tend to move quickly to capture the flashes of insight that pile up in my head as I read Scripture. If it resonates with me, I will add details to my mandala later.

Basic Drawings

Details added

7 Fine Art Resources for the Great Reversal

Here are the names of artists who have rendered interpretations of the great reversal sayings of Jesus. These are 2D works, i.e., paintings and drawings. These works can be used for inspiration. Feel free to go online and seek out your favorite imagery.

- The Birth of Jesus
    - *The Birth of Our Lord Jesus Christ,* James Tissot, Realism
    - *The Nativity,* Fra Angelico, Renaissance
    - *Hospitality Refused to the* Virgin *Mary and Joseph,* Jan Matsys, Renaissance
    - *The Nativity,* Tintoretto, Renaissance
- Love Your Enemies
    - *The Martyrdom of Saint Stephen,* Annibale Carracci, Baroque
    - *The Stoning of Saint Stephen,* Lorenzo Lotto, Renaissance
- Whoever Loses His or Her Life for My Sake
    - *Lord, Whither Goest Thou?,* Annibale Carracci, Baroque
- The Good Samaritan
    - *The Good Samaritan,* Vincent van Gogh, Post-Impressionism
    - *The Parable of the Good Samaritan,* Jan Wijnants, Dutch Golden Age
    - *The Good Samaritan,* Rembrandt, Baroque
    - *The Good Samaritan,* Josep Tapiro Baro, Orientalism
    - *The Good Samaritan,* Jacopo Bassano, Venetian School
- The Rich Fool
    - *The Man who Hoards,* James Tissot, Realism
- Where Your Treasure Is
    - *The Rich Young Man Went Away Sorrowful,* James Tissot, Realism
    - *For He Had Great Possessions,* George Frederick Watts, Symbolism
- First and Last
    - *The First Shall be Last,* James Tissot, Realism
    - *Jesus Washing Peter's Feet,* Ford Madox Brown, Pre-Raphaelite
- The Pharisee and the Tax Collector
    - *The Pharisee and the Publican,* James Tissot, Realism
    - *The Pharisee and the Publican,* Gustave Dore, Illustration/Printmaking
- More Blessed to Give than to Receive
    - *A La Fontaine,* William-Adolphe Bouguereau, Academic Art
    - *The Blind Girl,* John Everett Millais, Pre-Raphaelite
- The Penitent Thief on the Cross
    - *The Pardon of the Good Thief,* James Tissot, Realism
    - *Saint Dismas, the Good Thief,* Bradi Barth, Illustration
    - *Christ and the Good Thief,* Titian, Renaissance

8 Biblical Commentary and Symbolism Resources

Here are a few suggestions for Bible commentaries. Feel free to go online and seek out your favorite theologian. I have also included some references to Symbolism and Biblical Imagery.

1. Klyne R. Snodgrass, *Stories with Intent*: A Comprehensive Guide to the Parables of Jesus, 2008. Level: Intermediate to Advanced. At 864 pages, this is the most comprehensive commentary on the Parables of Jesus that I am aware of. Each parable is dealt with in detail, including an introduction, issues, comparison of the different Gospel writer accounts, cultural information, options for interpretation, and more. This is an excellent resource. Modern.

2. Robert H. Stein, *LUKE - The New American Commentary: An Exegetical and Theological Exposition of the Holy Scripture NIV Text*, 1992. Level: Intermediate. A strong Bible commentary on Luke. Very readable. Stein provides a short discussion, in the book's introduction, on the theme of the great reversal in Luke. Additionally, he highlights this recurrent theme throughout the commentary.

3. Jean Calvin Commentaries on the Bible: Harmony of the Evangelists, Matthew, Mark, and Luke. Mid-1500's. Level: Intermediate to Advanced. His theology is reformed. Calvin's genius is that he was one of the most outstanding biblical scholars that ever lived. He had a massive command of Scripture. His teaching feels as though it integrates all of Scripture. Note that these are Biblical commentaries. They are not a treatise on Calvinism. It may be found online.

4. Darrell L. Bock, *Luke, Baker Exegetical Commentary on the New Testament*, 1996. Level: Intermediate to Advanced. Considered one of the finest commentaries available on the Gospel of Luke. Over 2000 pages, this two-volume commentary is the most comprehensive commentary on Luke that I am aware of.

5. George Ferguson, *Signs and Symbols in Christian Art*, 1955. Later editions exist.

6. *Dictionary of Biblical Imagery*, 1998, General Editors: Leland Ryken, James C. Wilhoit, Tremper Longman III. Excellent essays on symbolism.

9 Online and Sharing Resources*

1. www.bestcommentaries.com for Bible commentary recommendations.

2. Jean Calvin commentaries can be found at: www.ccel.org/ccel/calvin/commentaries.i.html

3. http://www.studylight.org/commentary/ will get you to Verse-by-Verse Bible Commentary. Click on a book of the Bible. Next, click on a chapter, and finally, click on a verse. Several commentaries for the verse will then appear. This site is a very nice resource.

4. http://www.studylight.org/commentaries has links to a large number of online commentaries together with a brief description of the commentaries. Last check, there were links to over 80 online commentaries, including 45 whole Bible commentaries. Jean Calvin, Albert Barnes, John Bengel, and John Lightfoot are available here and recommended.

5. William Barclay and Matthew Henry commentaries may be found online. The best option is to use a search engine.

6. Symbols in Christian Art and Architecture can currently be found at: www.planetgast.net/symbols/

7. Symbol symbology is at: http://www.christiansymbols.net/. This site has been expanded and updated from time to time.

8. Mark Harden's Artchive, www.artchive.com/ftp_site.htm, summarizes close to 300 important artists from Altdorfer to Zurbaran. Biographies, summaries, articles, and images. Very nice site that has been around for years.

9. Bible Gateway, www.biblegateway.com, is a quick way to look up verses online, different translations or do keyword searches.

10. www.KerryPierce.com and www.ChristianMandalas.com for resources, FAQs, and links to sharing opportunities.

11. Blue Letter Bible, www.blueletterbible.org, online tools for advanced Bible students. Online videos show how to use the site.

*All websites are accurate at the time of this writing.